Classifying

Editor
Kim Fields

Editorial Project Manager
Mara Ellen Guckian

Editor-in-Chief
Sharon Coan, M.S. Ed.

Illustrators
Kelly McMahon
Reneé Christine Yates

Cover Artist
Brenda DiAntonis

Art Manager
Kevin Barnes

Art Director
CJae Froshay

Imaging
Ralph Olmedo, Jr.
James Edward Grace

Product Manager
Phil Garcia

Publisher
Mary D. Smith, M.S. Ed.

Author

Krista Pettit

Teacher Created Resources, Inc.
6421 Industry Way
Westminster, CA 92683
www.teachercreated.com

ISBN: 978-0-7439-3387-2

©2003 Teacher Created Resources, Inc.
Reprinted, 2012
Made in U.S.A.

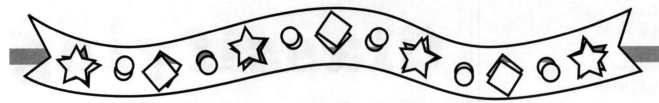

Table of Contents

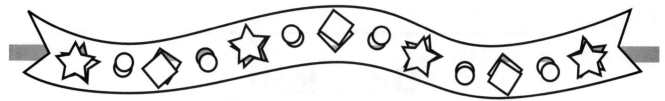

Introduction

Getting children ready for academic success should begin early. It is important, during these early years, to shape children's attitudes toward school and learning in a positive manner. Young children need frequent repetition and simplified directions. The activities should be engaging and visually stimulating. The purpose of this workbook series is to promote children's development and learning in an enjoyable way. Each activity book introduces young learners to new concepts and reinforces ones already learned.

In *Classification*, students will focus on the following concepts:

Matching—Children practice finding things that are the same.

Sorting—Children categorize things into groups, based on the differences among the objects.

Classifying—Children look at a group of objects and identify which object doesn't belong to the group.

Interpreting—After studying a scene, children decide what doesn't belong in the picture. The skill pages are great for enrichment, classroom practice, tutoring, home schooling, or just for fun. Parents can use this workbook series to reinforce skills learned at home and/ or school. Because some of the activities require cutting and pasting, photocopying these pages is suggested. Copying activities onto cardstock or heavy paper makes it easier for beginning cutters to grasp and manipulate the paper.

The series will enhance children's abilities to retain new skills. The series is a versatile resource and can benefit children in a variety of environments. The skill pages can be used for seatwork, homework, or home practice and feature easy-to-follow directions. This type of independent work gives children the support needed to internalize new concepts in an enjoyable and meaningful way.

Name _____

On a Roll

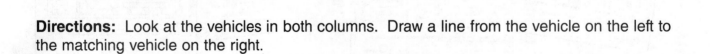

Directions: Look at the vehicles in both columns. Draw a line from the vehicle on the left to the matching vehicle on the right.

Name _____

The Big Top

Directions: Look at the circus performers. Color the matching pairs.

Name _____

On the Go

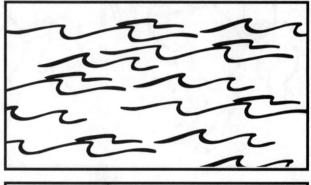

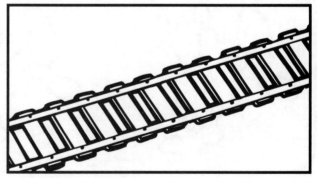

 •

Directions: Look at the vehicles on the left. Draw a line from each vehicle to the place where you would find it.

Name _____

Bow Wow House Hunt

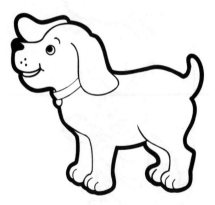

 ● ● ● ● ● ● ● ● ● ● ● ● ● ● ● ● ●

Directions: Look at the different sizes of dogs. Draw a line from each doghouse to a dog that fits.

Name _____

View Me

Directions: Look at the front of each animal. Draw a line to the matching back of the animal.

Name _____

Where Does It Go?

Directions: Look at the objects in both columns. Draw a line from each object to its matching container.

Name _____

It's My Job

Directions: Look at each vehicle. Draw a line from the vehicle to the person who would use it for work.

Name _____

Finishing Touches

✏ •

Directions: Look at each animal. Draw the missing parts needed to complete the animals.

In and Out

In   Out

Directions: Find the opposites. Draw a line from the **In** picture on the left to the matching **Out** picture on the right.

Name _____

Holiday Match

Directions: Look at both columns. Draw a line from each picture in the left column to the matching holiday symbol in the right column.

Name _____

Put Them Together

Directions: Cut out the pictures. Glue the *head* of each animal in box 1. Glue the *middle* of the matching animal in box 2. Glue the *end* of the animal in box 3.

Name _____

Snack Time

Directions: Cut out the peanuts. Glue the *big* peanuts beside Mama elephant. Glue the *small* peanuts beside Baby elephant.

Name _____

Shape Sort

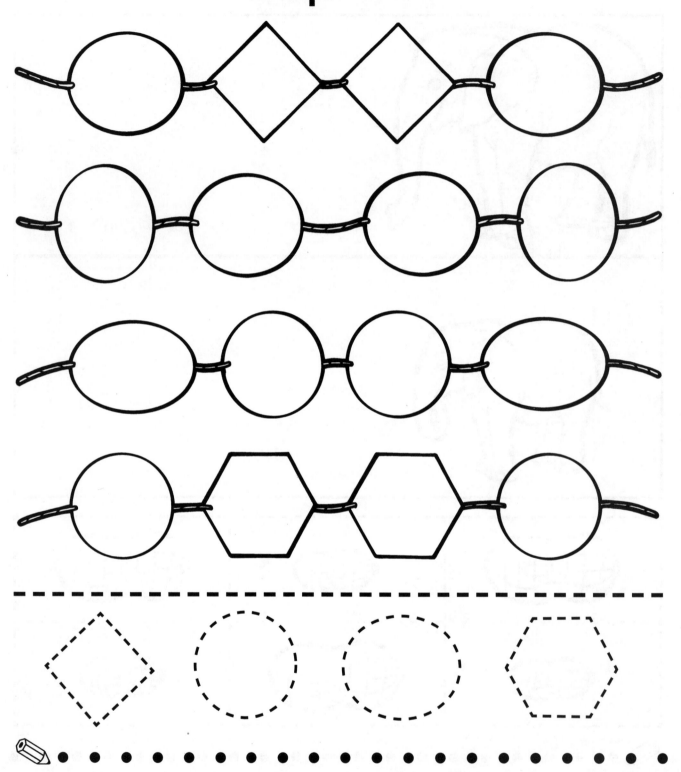

Directions: Cut out the beads. Glue each one on the matching bracelet. Color the bracelets.

Name _____

Make a Quilt

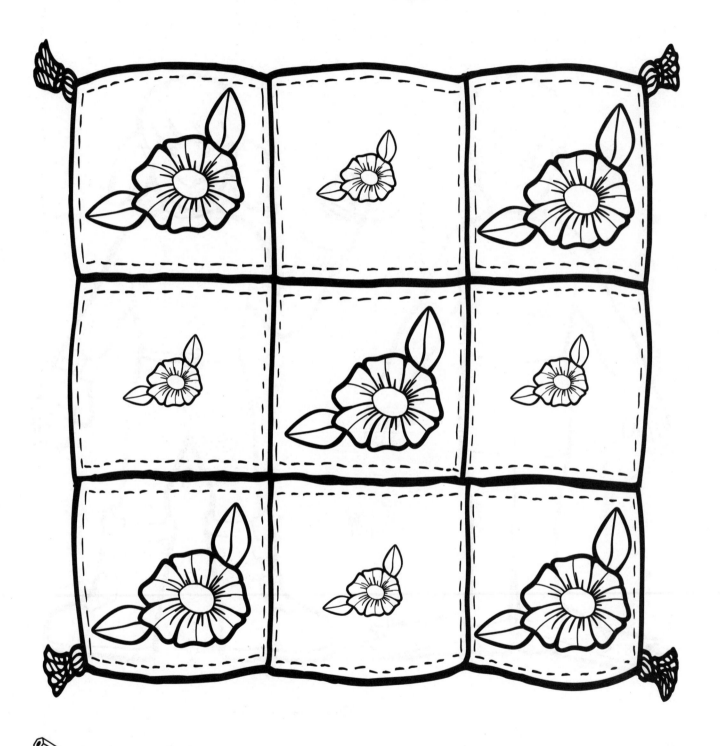

Directions: Use a blue crayon to color each flower that is *big*. Use a yellow crayon to color each flower that is *little*.

Name _____

What To Wear?

Directions: Cut out the paper dolls and the clothing on the following page. Finish dressing each paper doll with the appropriate clothing.

Name _____

What To Wear? (cont.)

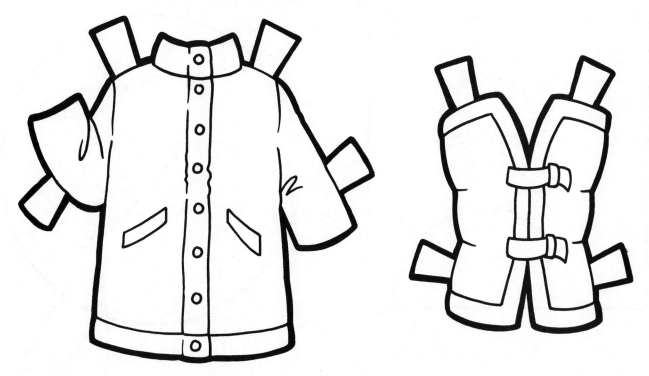

  • • • • • • • • • • • • • • • • •

Directions: Cut out the dolls on the previous page and the clothing on this page. Finish dressing each paper doll with the appropriate clothing.

Name _____

Shaping Up

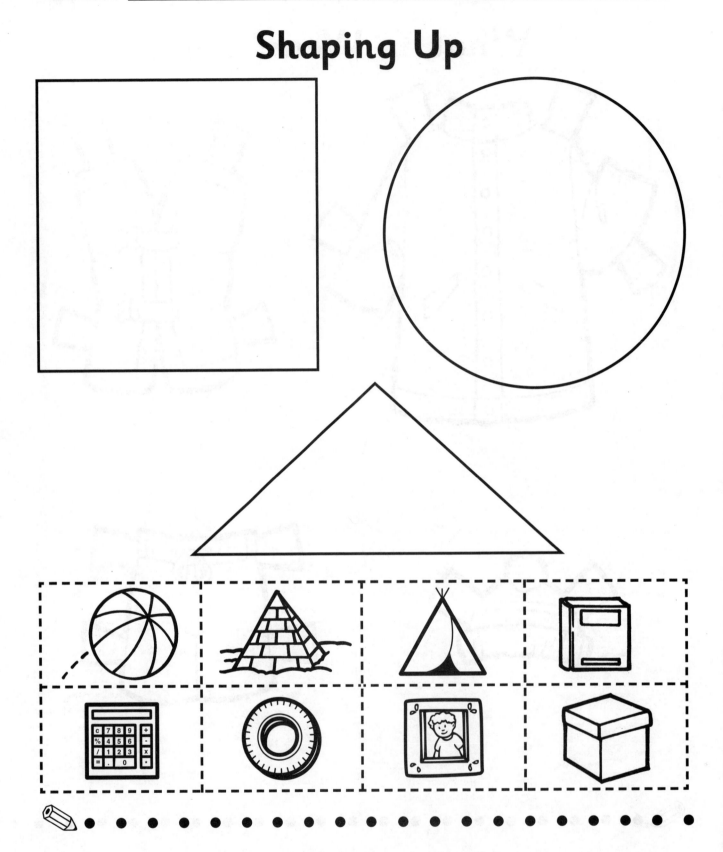

Directions: Cut out the pictures. Glue each picture on its matching shape.

Name _____

Tasty Treats

Directions: Cut out the pictures. Glue each food on the corresponding bag.

Size Sort

tall

short

Directions: Look at the pictures. Think about how big each object is in real life. Cut out each object and glue it in the corresponding box.

Name _____

Big Bug, Little Bug

big	little

Directions: Cut out the boxes. Glue each bug picture in the corresponding box. Talk about your choices.

Name _____

Habitat Hunt

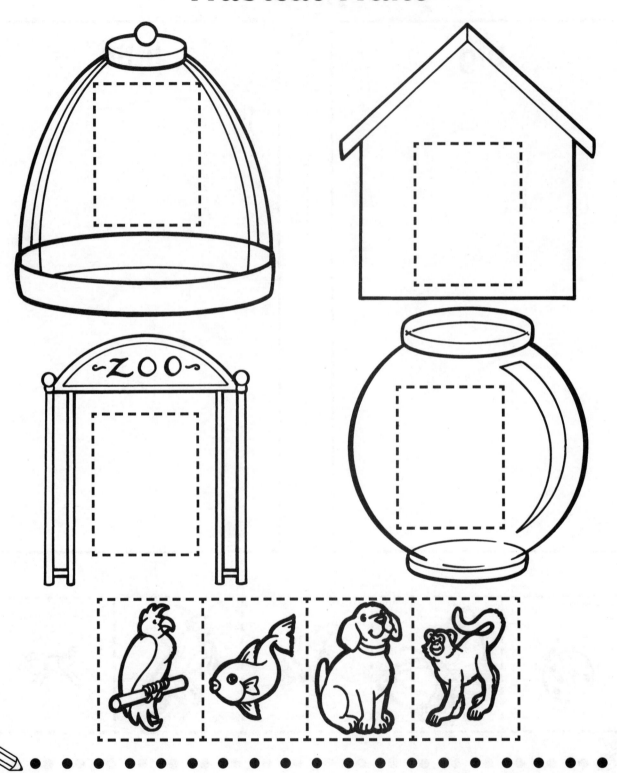

ZOO

Directions: Cut out each animal. Glue the animal inside the correct habitat. Talk about your choices.

Name _____

Choose the Tools

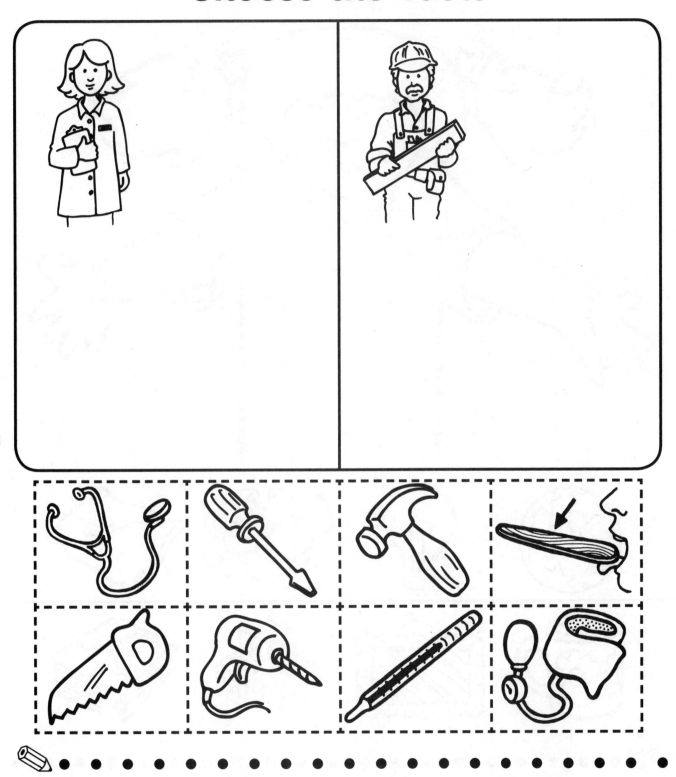

Directions: Cut out the tools. Decide which tools a doctor would use and which tools a construction worker would use. Glue each set of tools in the appropriate box.

Name _____

Careful Clara

Directions: Cut out the pictures. Glue each item in Clara's arms that would not break if dropped. Talk about your choices.

Name _____

Will It Float?

Directions: Cut out the pictures. Glue each object that would *sink* at the bottom of the tub. Glue each object that would *float* on the bubbles.

Name _____

All Mixed Up

Directions: Look at each row of pictures. There is a 1 in the box that shows what happens *first*. Write a 2 in the box that shows what happens *next*. Write a 3 in the box that shows what happens *last*.

Name _____

Cross It Out

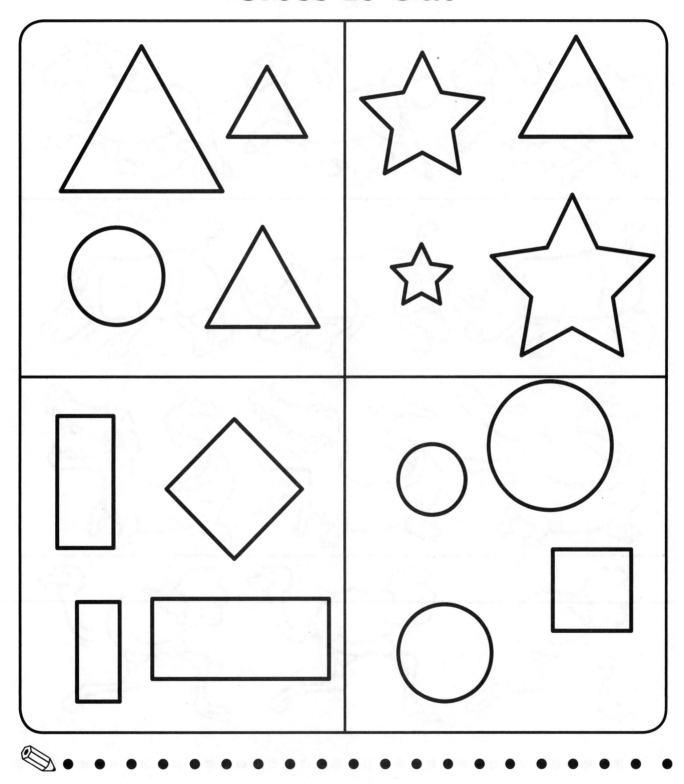

Directions: Look at each group of objects. Put an **X** on the one that does not belong.

Name _____

Odd One Out

Directions: Look at each group of animals. Circle the animal that is missing a part. Draw the missing part for the animal.

Name _____

Animal Find

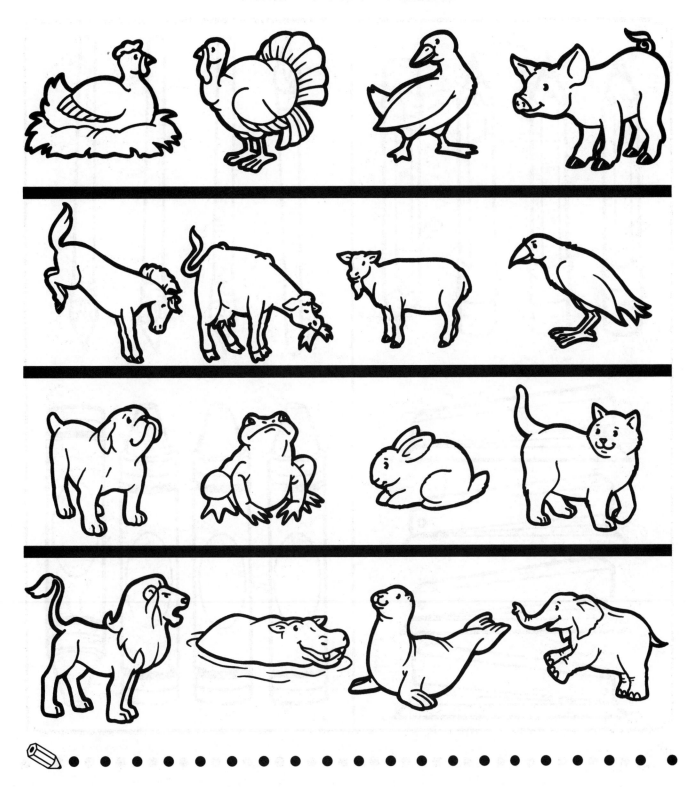

Directions: Look at the animals in each row. Color the animal that does not belong. Talk about your choices.

Name _____

Find Me

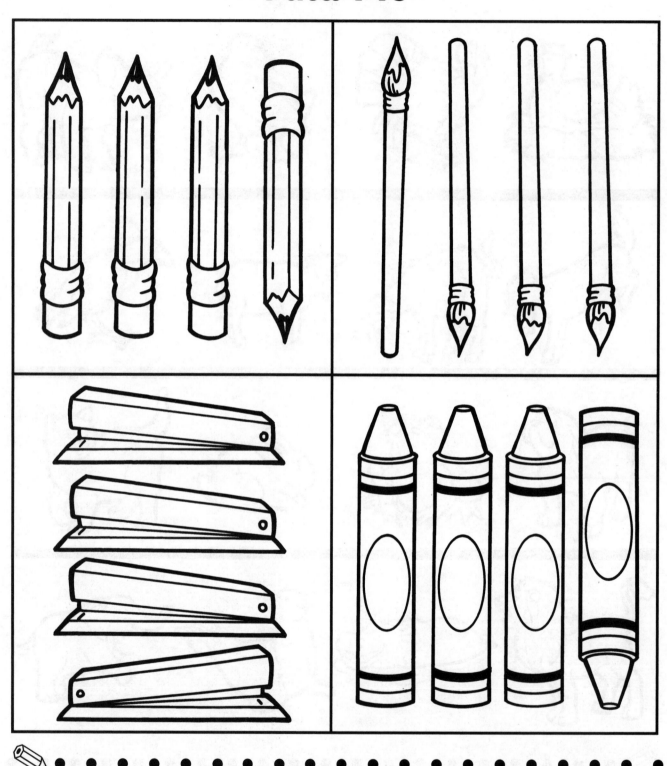

Directions: Look at each group of objects. Put an **X** on the object that is in a different position.

Name _____

Kitchen Mix Up

Directions: Look at the objects in each row. Cross out the object that does not belong in a kitchen.

Name _____

One Out

Directions: Look at each group of objects. Put an **X** on the object that does not belong.

Name _____

Classify Me!

| toys | pets | dogs | cars |

Directions: Cut out the words. Glue each word in the appropriate box.

Name _____

Head to Toe

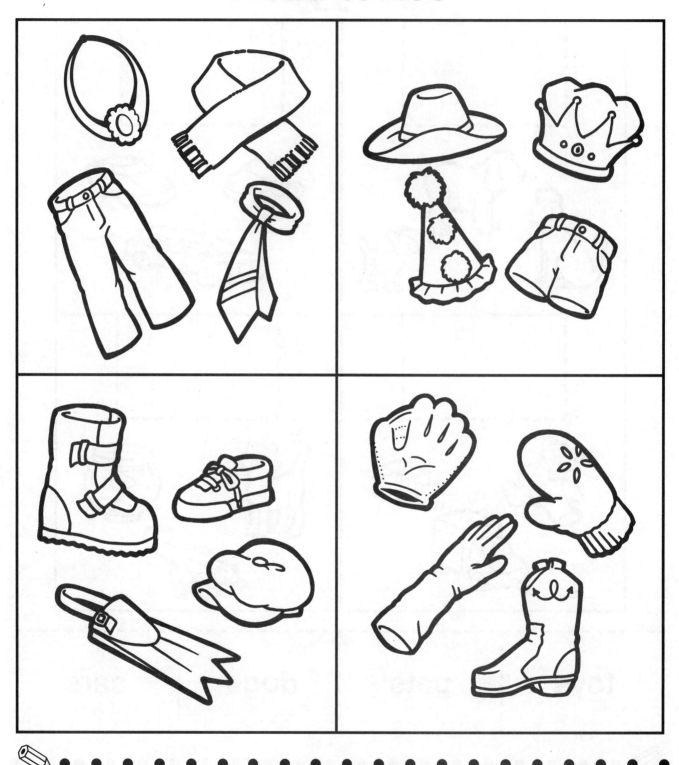

Directions: Look at the things in each box that you might wear. Circle the object in each group that does not belong.

Name _____

What Do I Make?

Directions: Look at the group of items with each worker. Put an **X** on the item that the worker would not make.

Name _____

Color Coding

Green

Red

Both

∅ •

Directions: Look at each section of the Venn diagram. Cross out each object that is *not* placed correctly within the diagram.

Name _____

Nature Fun

furry	rough	smooth

Directions: Cut out the words and pictures. Group the objects into 3 categories: *furry*, *rough*, or *smooth*. Glue the groups on another sheet of paper.

Name _____

Music, Music, Music

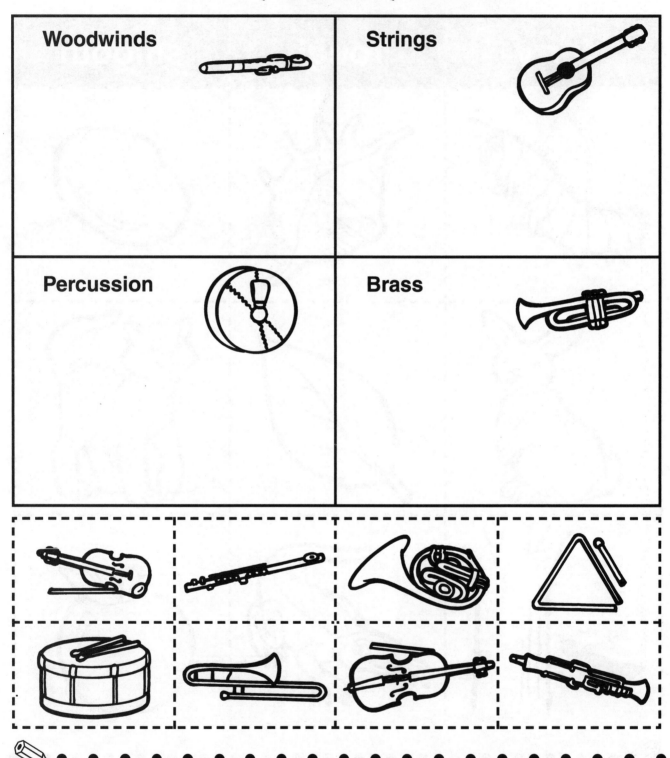

Directions: Cut out the instruments. Glue each one in the appropriate box. Talk about your choices.

Name _____

Piece of Cake

Directions: Look at the birthday cake. Cross out each item that does not belong on the cake.

Name _____

What's Wrong?

Mr. Bearly

2 + 8 =
4 + 6 =
9 + 1 =
11 - 1 =

✏️ •

Directions: Look at the classroom scene. Cross out each item that does *not* belong in a classroom. Talk about your choices.

Name _____

Room Check

Directions: Look at the bedroom scene. Cross out each item that does *not* belong in a bedroom. Talk about your choices.

Name _____

Playground Fix Up

Directions: Look at the playground scene. Cut out the pictures. Glue each object that belongs on a playground on the appropriate part of the scene. What does not belong in the playground?

Name _____

Fire Station Find

Directions: Look at the fire station. Circle each item that a firefighter would use. Talk about your choices.

Name _____

Amazing Amazon

Directions: Look at the jungle scene. Cut out the pictures and glue each object that belongs in a jungle on the scene.

Name _____

Summer Fun

Directions: Look at the summertime scene. Cut out the pictures and glue each object that you might find during the summer on the scene. Color the summertime picture.

Name _____

Winter Wonderland

Directions: Look at the wintertime scene. Color each item that you might find during a snowy, winter day. Talk about your choices.